2021

UK Rhymes

Edited By Roseanna Caswell

First published in Great Britain in 2021 by:

 Young**Writers**®
— Est. 1991 —

Young Writers
Remus House
Coltsfoot Drive
Peterborough
PE2 9BF
Telephone: 01733 890066
Website: www.youngwriters.co.uk

Printed and bound in the UK by BookPrintingUK
Website: www.bookprintinguk.com
YB0476C

FOREWORD

Dear Reader,

Welcome to this book packed full of feathery, furry and scaly friends!

Young Writers' Poetry Safari competition was specifically designed for 5-7 year-olds as a fun introduction to poetry and as a way to think about the world of animals. They could write about pets, exotic animals, dinosaurs or even make up their own crazy creature! From this starting point, the poems could be as simple or as elaborate as the writer wanted, using imagination and descriptive language.

Given the young age of the entrants, we have tried to include as many poems as possible. Here at Young Writers we believe that seeing their work in print will inspire a love of reading and writing and give these young poets the confidence to develop their skills in the future. Poetry is a wonderful way to introduce young children to the idea of rhyme and rhythm and helps learning and development of communication, language and literacy skills.

These young poets have used their creative writing abilities, sentence structure skills, thoughtful vocabulary and most importantly, their imaginations, to make their poems and the animals within them come alive. I hope you enjoy reading them as much as we have.

CONTENTS

Martin Miles (7)	70	Kye Saavan Shipp (7)	110
Elliott Gordon-Leaf (6)	71	Verity Taylor (7)	111
Keilija Kruze (6)	72	Misha Ffrench (7)	112
Cara Sim (7)	73	Rose Gurney (7)	113
Bella (7)	74	William McCauley-	114
Loki Pedley (6)	75	Tinniswood (7)	
Evie-Rose Sharpe (6)	76	Eoin O'Brien (7)	115
Lucas G (5)	77	Evie Wheaton (7)	116
Shaylene Burbidge (6)	78	Isabelle Baldwin (7)	117
Lilly Higgins (6)	79	Shivani Mistry (7)	118
Jessica Brown (6)	80	Dominic Butler (7)	119
Olivia Graham (5)	81	Nimrit Sindher (6)	120
Chiril Bulubica (5)	82	Aryun Rabheru (6)	121
Grace Mitchell (6)	83	Ronnie Bannister (7)	122
Alayah Montgomery (5)	84	Erin Long (7)	123
Layla Ruffel (5)	85	Sofia Rai (7)	124
Brooklyn Cooper-Mason (5)	86	Arjan Auluck (7)	125
Livvi Pedley (6)	87	Andrey Olney (9)	126
John Montgomery (6)	88	Henry Stere (7)	127
Martins Vecais (5)	89	Maisie Lockyer (6)	128
Bianca Caraus (6) & Catrina	90	Karamvir Singh Athwal (7)	129
Lacie-Mae Moore (6)	91		
Dominik Swidrski (6)	92		
Alise Silina (6)	93		
Charlie London (7)	94		
Samantha Eliza Kreslina (7)	95		

Bishopsgate School, Englefield Green

Sophie Nicholson (7)	96
Yuvi Uppal (6)	97
Isobel Massie (7)	98
Marla Johal (7)	99
Charl Marais (7)	100
Grayson Webb (7)	101
Joshua Dean (7)	102
Simran Kapila (6)	103
Henry Stannard (7)	104
Ruby Carver (7)	105
Joshua Jacobi (7)	106
Lian Louw (7)	107
Diya Khosla (6)	108
Claudia Priestley (7)	109

Marton Primary Academy, Marton

Hephzibah A (6)	130
Mylee J (6)	131
Annabelle B (6)	132
Olivia S (6)	133
Presley Marshall (6)	134
Ellie C (6)	135
Fatoumatta C (6)	136
Caleb H (6)	137
Henry A (5)	138
Elizabeth H (5)	139
Hugo Hoogerwerf (6)	140
Matilda H (6)	141
Amelia M (6)	142
Haniel A (6)	143
Lexie Fox (5)	144
Lenny Gelder (6)	145
Maizie B (5)	146
Logan M (6)	147
Jake M (6)	148

Dylan-James Brannan (6)	149
Imogen Phillips (5)	150
Alysia Mccoy (6)	151
Kyle M (6)	152

Shakespeare Primary School, Fleetwood

Evan Moran (7)	153
Cody Kennedy (7)	154
Amity Crellin (7)	156
Zac Newton (7)	158
Summer Hill (7)	160
Jaxon Smith (7)	161
Teddy Bamber (7)	162
Sophie Myers (7)	163
Carson Stone (6)	164
Raya Yordanova (6)	165
Olivia Coe (7)	166
Toby Smith	167
Corey (7)	168
Harley Holt (7)	169
Jenson Gray (6)	170
Millie Potter (7)	171
Sophie Davies (7)	172
Jackson Armstrong (7)	173
Eliza Magowan (6)	174
Amelia Whiteshide-Shaw (6)	175
Elijah Armstrong (6)	176
Emilia Maricic (5)	177
Holly Emslie (6)	178
Reuben Yardley (6)	179
Beth Williamson (6)	180
Rose Stirzaker (6)	181

Springfield Primary School, Sunbury-On-Thames

Janvika Jagadeesh (5)	182
Max Honey (7)	183
Prem Chouhan (7)	184
Leah Midwinter (7)	185
Dominic Germishuys (7)	186
Leila Aghel (7)	187

Sophie O'Donnell (5)	188
Zainab Naqvi (6)	189
James Lee (6)	190

St Mary's Primary School Dunsford, Ardglass

Annie McConville (7)	191
Nicole Karbauske (7)	192
Isla O'Connor (7)	193
James McGreevy (7)	194
Izzy Burns (7)	195
Stella Zych (7)	196
Madden McEvoy (7)	197
Callum Moreland (7)	198
Amelia Feenan (7)	199
Eabha O'Connor (6)	200

Westwood Primary School, Leeds

Charlie Wood (5)	201
Wyatt Hitchcox (6)	202
Bobby Keeligan (6)	203
Blake Scaife (6)	204
Rose Cummings (6)	205
Lucii Batley-Hewitt (5)	206
Harley Cross (6)	207
Tilly Gudgeon (7)	208
Aleksei Beloussov (6)	209
Tyreece Whitley (6)	210
Mutiat Kumoye (6)	211
Mia Hart-Kumar (6)	212
BooBoo Hallas (6)	213
George Richardson (6)	214
Jacob Egan (7)	215
Amelia Holmes (6)	216
Joey Baker (6)	217
George Kenyon (6)	218
Deacon Massey (6)	219
TreydenThomas Appleyard (7)	220
Leo Brummitt (6)	221
Lorna Walton (5)	222
Ebonie Wager (6)	223
Sam Avison (7)	224

The Poems

Cheetahs

Cheetahs are the fastest land mammal on the planet
They are the third-fastest animal on the planet
Before the peregrine falcon and the eagle
Cheetahs can outrun the fastest man on the planet, Usain Bolt
Cheetahs can run at a top speed of 71mph
Their bones feel like bird bones, not cat bones
Which makes them fast
When they put their foot down their claws dig into the ground
And when they push forward they cross 7 metres
They are very good at turning sharp corners.

Shammah Maparanyanga (7)
Beanfield Primary School, Corby

The Very Beautiful Butterfly

My creature is a colourful butterfly.

She has lots of friends with lots of colours.
My butterfly is the best.

She can hide from her friends.

She likes to say *zzzz!*
She likes to dance with her friends.

She doesn't go upside down.
She eats rainbow lollipops.

She likes to do backflips.

She is silly all day.
She plays with her friends.

She looks like a scarecrow.
She eats scary slugs.

Kianna Carbon (5)
Beanfield Primary School, Corby

Monkey Man

My creature is a monkey
His name is Bananas
He stinks but has a very big heart
It has a baby and it's very ugly
I called him Bananas
Because he loves bananas
He lives on Planet Banana
He only eats bananas
He looks like a crazy monkey
But he is very friendly, trust me
All he does is sits on the toilet
And reads his comic
It is called 'The Tales of Spider-Man'
He plays Fortnite a lot
He is a pro at it.

Jakesy Rafferty (6)
Beanfield Primary School, Corby

The Very Beautiful Butterfly

My creature is a colourful butterfly
She has lots of friends with lots of colourful
colours
My butterfly is the best
She can hide from her friends
She likes to fly
She likes to dance with her friends
She doesn't go upside down
She eats rainbow lollipops
She even eats oranges
She is silly all day
She plays with her friends
She looks at scary snakes
She eats scary slugs
And she eats bananas and lemons.

Ryleigh Ellis (6)
Beanfield Primary School, Corby

4

A Little Grasshopper

G rilly is his silly name

R unning is what he likes to do

A little hop there and here

S o he never stops hopping

S o, he even hops in his dreams

H ere and there, a little everywhere

"O h!" he says when he is a little chilly

P is for Panny, his brother

P anny is his nanny all day

E is for he eats

R eferee is for bedtime!

Betuel Ohue (7)
Beanfield Primary School, Corby

Bell The Dog

She's a lovely doggy
Loves balls
She plays with them all the time
Nice dog, never bites
Only plays with balls
Likes to sleep
Loves her owner
Never wants to leave her home
She can dance and sing
Her favourite food is chocolate
Her favourite drink is milk
Never wants to leave her owner
Loves her owner too much
Always sleeps with her owner and likes it.

Lexi Eaveson (7)
Beanfield Primary School, Corby

Magnificent Koalas

Koalas have cute round eyes,
On the top of trees they search for the
eucalyptus leaves.
While other animals are hunting,
They are relaxing in the trees eating
eucalyptus leaves.
A koala is grey and soft, they are also very
fluffy,
Lots of eucalyptus leaves are eaten all day
long.
Always sleeping like a sloth,
Sometimes they climb high in the trees.

Alyssa Pearcey (7)

Beanfield Primary School, Corby

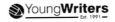
Magnificent Koalas

Koalas have cute round eyes
In trees, koalas are relaxing in the hot sun
While other animals are hunting, koalas are relaxing
All animals are cute but koalas are the best
Loving, grey, fluffy koalas are the best kind of koalas
All koalas have sharp claws but they're also very messy
Some koalas are very sensitive
They can die if it is too hot.

Isabella Lungu (7)
Beanfield Primary School, Corby

A Very Pretty Butterfly

A butterfly is adorable
Its name is Stella
She loves to eat pollen
My creature is a butterfly
She is red and pink
My butterfly is cute and adorable
My butterfly likes to play and flap
My butterfly flies to school and goes to
learn
My butterfly has a baby
Its name is Molly
My butterfly is in the sky
She loves to flap and flap.

Julieanne Smart (6)
Beanfield Primary School, Corby

Cute Sloths

S loths are cute, cuddly and very slow

L ots of sloths mostly live in huge jungles or rainforests, they are adorable

O h my goodness, sloths are so cute, I'm going to explode!

T he sloths mostly live in huge jungles and rainforests

H ow many sloths are there in the jungle?

S loths are so cute, I want one as a pet.

Parker Johnson (6)
Beanfield Primary School, Corby

Beautiful Penguins

My penguins are beautiful
My penguins are pink and blue
My penguins are princesses
My penguins live in a castle
My penguins are cute
My penguins like to eat cotton candy
My penguins are called Lilly, Lacie and
Chloe
My penguins are lovely
I love my penguins
My penguins love me
My penguins are with me all the time.

Ezmai Kirkwood (6)
Beanfield Primary School, Corby

Guess My Wild Animal!

My animal smells like bananas, insects and just stinky
My animal looks kind, his eyes are happy and friendly
My animal sounds sometimes every day like a very noisy party with fireworks
My animal feels like velvet, all soft and cuddly
My animal tastes like sausages and ham, his favourite snacks
I love my animal, my monkey!

Sophia Burt (7)
Beanfield Primary School, Corby

Dogicorn

The dogicorn is small
It likes to eat ice cream
It likes sleeping and watching TV
Because it is lazy
It always likes jumping on me
So it doesn't get hurt
I always catch it
Because it is beautiful
My pet dogicorn is cute and smart
Because it knows
Maths, English, phonics and handwriting.

Maria Krygier (7)
Beanfield Primary School, Corby

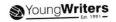

The Very Old Cat

My creature is a cat
She is black and white
She is fluffy
She has sharp teeth
And rolls on the grass
She runs fast
She eats cat food
She lives in my house
She is cute
She is happy
She has sharp claws
She likes to climb
She goes on people's tummies
And always purrs.

Vuk Pejic (6)
Beanfield Primary School, Corby

All About Dolphins

D olphin is a good dolphin that listens to people

O n June the 15th is her birthday

L emon is her favourite juice

P ink is her favourite colour

H er friends are coming to her birthday

I n June, she will invite her cousins

N ear her house, she plants seaweed.

Maya Belostocka (7)
Beanfield Primary School, Corby

Fun Animals

L ions are fierce and scary

I bet the lions are eating right now, but first, they will creep up on the other animals

O n the day the lion was born, it was so cute, it had to have its dinner

N o one has seen that it is so big and pounced on the biggest animal ever. It left the bones behind.

Elsie Smart (6)

Beanfield Primary School, Corby

Cat In A Cave

C ats are cute, but mean too because they hiss, scratch and sleep. They are cute when they sleep

A nd it eats rocks, fruit, vegetables, leaves and grass

T he cat lives in a cave. It's nocturnal. It sleeps all day. It hunts at night. It also lives in a house if it breaks in. It likes the dark.

Phoebe Johnson (6)
Beanfield Primary School, Corby

The Nice Panda Bear

My panda bear likes to sit in the sun
He has lots of sharp teeth
He has a black spot on his tummy
He is cute
He is the best at hiding
He likes to sit in the sun
He talks to his friends
He likes to eat bamboo
It is his favourite
He likes to dance with friends
And he is kind.

Louie Byles (6)
Beanfield Primary School, Corby

Dineagle

D inosaur eagle that is giant
I t flies a lot of the time
N eeds to have 50 pieces of food each day
E ats all animals, but not humans
A ll the time, it looks at the clouds
G oes to eat in the morning
L oves eating foxes
E ats lots of things.

Matei Conut (7)
Beanfield Primary School, Corby

Wild Animal

M y animal can be crazier than a lion.

O ur animals are calm and cute.

N o other animal is like it.

K eepers look after the monkey and keep them safe.

E very monkey likes to eat bananas.

Y ou will never see a cuter animal. Some monkeys are cuter than a baby.

Poppy Blair (7)

Beanfield Primary School, Corby

Cute Tigers

T igers are cute, scary and they can camouflage

I like that tigers are like big fluffy teddies with chocolate

G et away you scary, mean tiger! It is coming to eat me

E at meat like deer and wildebeest

R oaring is loud

S uper fast when they are running.

Keeleigh Joseph (7)

Beanfield Primary School, Corby

Narwhals

Narwhals are cute, narwhals are cool
You would never find one in a pool
They eat krill which penguins also kill
The krill tries to swim
But the penguins and narwhals are too fast
The narwhals and penguins went to have a feast
And said to each other, "You're the best!"

Sophie Croll (7)
Beanfield Primary School, Corby

The Penguin Goes Bananas!

Penguins love to play with friends
They play all the time
They play football all the time together
And play hide-and-seek
They love to run and make fun all the time
They like to rhyme and play
They like to make slime and eat lime
They go zzz and eat fish and waddle.

Priya Saini (6)
Beanfield Primary School, Corby

Tiger's Favourite Stuff

My creature is a tiger
He has lots of stripes
He lives in Africa
And likes to stay in the woods
He likes to eat meat
He likes playing hide-and-seek
With his friends
My creature likes to go for a walk
And his friends like to come
To Tiger's cave for a party.

Isabella Jaroni (6)
Beanfield Primary School, Corby

The Turtle Elephant Panda

My creature is a slow creature
He has lots of lovely friends
He lives in the sea
And likes to eat bamboo
He likes to play hide-and-seek
He thinks that he can hide the best
My creature likes to play
And he is very, very funny
My creature is a turtle elephant panda.

Bence Szabo (6)
Beanfield Primary School, Corby

My Bee Called Lucy, Amber Or Betty

B etty, my cute little bee, loves to play but she is still a little bee

E nters her beehive most times to make honey or take a nap to get some more energy

E ntertained most at six to seven and sometimes learns new tricks. You can call my cute bee Lucy, Amber or Betty.

Emma Glackin (6)
Beanfield Primary School, Corby

The Spotty And Pink Bear

My bear talks a lot with his bear friends
My bear lives in Pink Land and in a pink
house
She has lots of bear friends
She is a pink, spotty bear
She likes to dance
She is a chubby and cute bear
She is the best at hide-and-seek
She likes to play at the park.

Beau Baillie (6)
Beanfield Primary School, Corby

Lily Anna The Giraffe

My giraffe is very cheeky
My giraffe is very dirty
My giraffe eats grass and ice cream
My giraffe is very cute and nice
My giraffe loves playing on the grass
My giraffe is called Lily Anna
My giraffe likes houses and rainbows
My giraffe lives on a farm.

Faith Odili (7)
Beanfield Primary School, Corby

The Mysterious Monkey

Monkeys can be very quiet
And go *oo, aa, aa* loudly
This monkey is not loud
It is mysterious
Sometimes, this monkey can be loud
The monkey eats lots of bananas
It is exactly the same as the other monkeys
But this monkey eats lots of bananas.

Branden Webb (7)
Beanfield Primary School, Corby

Fun Safari

Tigers are really fast
Tigers can smell food in their sleep
It pounces out of the tree
If it sees another animal
It has sharp claws
To scratch other animals
It's orange and black
It eats meat, animals and insects
It tastes the animals.

Diana Coman (6)
Beanfield Primary School, Corby

The Funniest Sloth In The World

S loths are the funniest animals in the world

L ots of sloths are funny and try to get leaves from the top of the tree

O n top of the trees, the sloths hide

T hey like climbing up the trees

H unting for crunchy leaves and fruit.

Oliver Moat (6)

Beanfield Primary School, Corby

My Friend, Rhino

Rhinos smell like mud, sweat and water
He is very stinky
Rhinos look grey, smooth
And like a rock with horns
Rhinos sound like a bug with no mouth
Rhinos feel smooth and wet
Rhinos taste like a rotten banana
And really hard toffee!

Max James (7)
Beanfield Primary School, Corby

Smooth, Pretty Elephant

My creature is an elephant
He has yellow soft skin
He lives in the woods
And he likes to drink water

He likes to eat doughnuts
He thinks about snakes for its dinner
My creature likes to dance and sing
And likes to sleep.

Finley Buchanan (6)
Beanfield Primary School, Corby

Litten, You Are Cute

Oh, Litten, Litten, why are you called Litten?
Because you are a Pokémon kitten
I love you
You are red and black
I have some Poké treats for you!
I like Ash
You live with Ash
All you do is sleep forever and ever!

Oscar Lewis (6)
Beanfield Primary School, Corby

Jungle Safari

T igers are fast like lightning

I like tigers so much because they are very fast

G rass is very long for tigers

E verywhere, tigers are hunting

R oaring tigers everywhere

S nakes are killing tigers.

Oskar Jadczuk (7)
Beanfield Primary School, Corby

Cheeky Joe The Monkey

M y monkey is very cuddly

O nly eats bananas and insects

N aughty and rather cheeky

K eep on climbing to get lots of bananas

E nergetic monkey running and climbing

Y ummy fruit in his rumbly belly.

Rudy Gray (6)

Beanfield Primary School, Corby

The Lovely, Colourful Dolphin

My creature is a dolphin
She has rainbow skin
She lives in the big sea
And she loves me

She likes to eat seagrass doughnuts
She thinks she wants to be a butterfly
My creature likes to dance
And will never leave me.

Gracie Goodes (6)
Beanfield Primary School, Corby

My Pretty Giraffe

My creature is a kind giraffe
He is a kind of slow giraffe
He lives in the jungle
And the zoo

He likes to eat grass
He thinks that he is alone
My creature likes to walk and talk
And walk everywhere in the jungle.

Alfie Fazackarley (6)
Beanfield Primary School, Corby

Elephant

My creature is an elephant
She is bumpy
She lives in the zoo
She sleeps in the zoo
She likes to eat meat
She thinks that she's a dog
And she barks
My creature likes to suck up water
And she likes to spray.

Penney Watson (6)
Beanfield Primary School, Corby

The Penguin

My creature is a penguin
She has lots of ice rakes
She lives in the Arctic
And sleeps under the water
She likes to eat fish
She thinks we are friends
My creature likes to go underwater
And likes to go on ice lakes.

Sophie Lofty (6)
Beanfield Primary School, Corby

The Lion Is A Wild Animal

My creature is a lion
She has lots of shiny fur
She lives with her family under the rocks
She is a wild animal
She likes to eat meat
She thinks of a beautiful place
My creature loves her family
And her children.

Emilia Ieromenko (6)
Beanfield Primary School, Corby

Cute Monkey

My creature is a monkey
She has lots of fluff
She lives in a tree
And she sleeps on a branch
She likes to eat bananas
She thinks of bananas
My creature likes to make up games
My monkey plays with her friends.

Calissa Mallett (6)
Beanfield Primary School, Corby

A Story Of A Silly Butterfly

My insect is a colourful butterfly
She has lots of colourful eyes
She lives in the woods
And likes to dance

She likes to eat rainbow ice cream
She thinks of dancing
My insect likes to fly
And eat.

Halle Bell (6)
Beanfield Primary School, Corby

The Monster

My creature is a monster
He has a ship
He lives in a cave
And he likes to kill

He likes to eat meat
He thinks of dancing
My creature likes to
Watch the Nintendo Switch
And he likes to bite.

David Falconer (6)
Beanfield Primary School, Corby

Catacorn

C ute and lazy
A cool catacorn
T ired all of the time
A crobat, a bit
C urious little catacorn
O bedient
R eady for bed
N ot that ready for an activity.

Aliza Watson (7)
Beanfield Primary School, Corby

Cheetah

Cheetah Boom! Boom! Boom!
The super-fast cheetah
Cheetah is super-fast. Boom! Boom! Boom!
Yellowish Cheetah
Teacher? No, it's a fast cheetah
A cheetah? How fast?
Super fast
Yay, yellowish Cheetah.

Hans Uzoma (7)

Beanfield Primary School, Corby

Exciting Safari

L ions are loud because they roar a lot on the dry land

I think lions are the king of the animals

O nly they defend themselves from other animals

N o animal can take the crown from the lion.

Diidh Dumi (7)

Beanfield Primary School, Corby

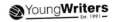

My Cheetah

My creature is a cheetah
She has lots of fur
She lives in the jungle
And sleeps on the grass
She likes to eat meat
She thinks about food
My creature likes to hunt
And she likes to eat creatures.

Ava Ratcliffe (6)
Beanfield Primary School, Corby

The Dangerous Cheetah

My animal is a cheetah
He has skills
He lives in the jungle
And he can run
He likes to eat chocolate ice cream
He thinks about explosions
My animal likes to run in the jungle
And likes to sing.

Oliver Mason (6)
Beanfield Primary School, Corby

Dinosaur Who Jumps

My creature is a dinosaur
She has a long neck and long legs
She lives in the wild
And she is big
She likes to eat leaves
She thinks about meat
My creature likes to jump up
And likes to fight.

Samuel Mason (6)
Beanfield Primary School, Corby

Little Lamb

My creature is a baby lamb
She has lots of fur
She lives in a very big field
And she loves grass
She likes to eat hay
And thinks having friends is nice
My creature likes to run
And it plays.

Matilda Dunmore (6)
Beanfield Primary School, Corby

Dragon

D amp dragon, smelly, creepy
R aging dragon killing people
A ble to eat every day
G rim, big, grumpy, uppity
O range dragon hunts gorillas
N ever happy dragon.

Noah Chalmers (7)
Beanfield Primary School, Corby

The Normal Elephant

My creature is a normal elephant
He has lots of grey skin
He lives in the forest or in a zoo
He is stompy
He likes to eat grass
He thinks he is special
My creature likes to stomp and walk.

Danielis Gedvilas (6)
Beanfield Primary School, Corby

Dinosaurs

Dangerous T-rex
He was in the trees
He was cold in the snow
He was hot in the sun
There were lots and lots of dinosaurs
He had very sharp teeth
He saw a tree
He is very dangerous.

Sebastian Andrei Huiban (7)
Beanfield Primary School, Corby

The Robot Shark

My sea creature is a robot shark
He has robot parts
He lives in the ocean
He likes to eat cheeseburgers
He thinks about cheeseburgers
My animal likes to be tough
And scares people.

Carson Lewis (6)
Beanfield Primary School, Corby

Cute Bunny

My creature is a bunny
She has lots of carrots
She lives in the jungle
And she likes the jungle
She likes to eat lots of carrots
She thinks about jumping
My creature likes jumping.

Max Gvazdauskas (6)
Beanfield Primary School, Corby

Brown, Scared Sausage Dog

My animal is a sausage dog
He is scared all the time
He likes to eat sausages
He likes to run a lot
He lives in a dog house
He thinks about me
He is funny
He is very fluffy.

Willow Warrener (6)
Beanfield Primary School, Corby

The Unicorn That Is Nice

My animal is a unicorn
She has a lot of magic
She lives in Unicorn Land
And she has fun

She likes to eat doughnuts
She thinks of doughnuts
My animal likes to play Roblox.

Peyton Smith (5)
Beanfield Primary School, Corby

Sleepy Sloth

Sloths like to climb trees
Sloths move really slow
Sloths eat very slowly
Sloths like to sleep
Sloths have big eyes
Sloths like to smell food
Sloths like to taste leaves.

Demi-Leigh Clark (7) & Patrick Artagea (6)

Beanfield Primary School, Corby

Noisy Pig

My creature is a pig
She makes lots of noise
She lives on a farm
And she sleeps in the mud
She likes to eat apples
My creature likes to play in the mud
And go for rides.

Isaac Brocklesby (6)
Beanfield Primary School, Corby

The Cow

My animal is a cute cow
He has a cute face
He lives on a farm
And eats grass all day
He thinks about the moon
My animals like to be funny
And he loves to be silly.

Nektarios Luca (6)
Beanfield Primary School, Corby

Fun Safari

They have a long neck
They are bigger than a tree
They munch on leaves and grass
They smell like leaves
Because its head is in the trees
They like eating the leaves.

Junior Sharman (7)
Beanfield Primary School, Corby

A Poem About My Dog, Luna

My cute dog, Luna
My cute dog, Luna, is silly
My cute dog, Luna, is cute
My cute dog, Luna, is running
My cute dog, Luna, is jumping
My cute dog, Luna, is funny.

Alexis McIntosh (6)
Beanfield Primary School, Corby

A Beautiful Murcitty

A beautiful mercitty is under the sea
It eats crab and seaweed
The starfish bully it sometimes
But she doesn't care
Because she's my beautiful mercitty.

Ebony Magee (6)
Beanfield Primary School, Corby

The Funniest Sloth In The World

Sloths are the funniest animal
They smell leaves
Sloths are cute and funny
Lots of sloths are funny
They eat lots of grass and leaves
They climb up trees.

Brody Hall
Beanfield Primary School, Corby

Loud Pecker

P ecks all the wood
E ats wood
C atches lots of wood
K eeps on pecking
E very woodpecker eats wood
R eally fast.

Finley (7)
Beanfield Primary School, Corby

Moo Moo Woof

My creature is a cow
She has lots of spots
She lives on a farm
She likes to eat grass
She thinks she's a dog
My creature likes to eat and drink.

Arya Miskovic-McMichael (6)
Beanfield Primary School, Corby

The Lion

L stands for the yellow lion

I stands for in a zoo

O stands for on the long grass

N stands for not allowed to be out of his cage.

Rhys Young (7)
Beanfield Primary School, Corby

Rocky

He is annoying every time
He eats ham, oranges and pizza
He annoys me all the time
I go to sleep but he is awake
He is not cool
And not amazing.

Eryk Awgul (7)
Beanfield Primary School, Corby

An Animal

My animal can taste leaves
My animal can smell like leaves and trees
My animal looks kind and cute
It feels soft and furry
It sounds quiet and loud.

Martin Miles (7)
Beanfield Primary School, Corby

Cheetah

My creature is a cheetah
She has lots of dots on her back
She lives in the trees at night-time
She eats lots of meat
She likes to run really fast.

Elliott Gordon-Leaf (6)
Beanfield Primary School, Corby

Sunny Safari

Giraffes sound quiet and calm
Giraffes smell like fresh cheese
Giraffes look kind and friendly
Giraffes feel soft
Giraffes taste like ice cream.

Keilija Kruze (6)
Beanfield Primary School, Corby

All About Horses

H is for high

O is for enormous

R is for brown

S is for stinky, it smells like grass

E is for elegant fur.

Cara Sim (7)

Beanfield Primary School, Corby

Unicorn

Unicorns are the greatest
And there is a family
I am obsessed with unicorns
It is cute
Unicorn
And it is royal
Unicorns are good.

Bella (7)
Beanfield Primary School, Corby

Giraffe

My creature is a giraffe
He has a lot of stripes
He lives in the zoo
Leaves and bushes he likes to eat too
He likes to look around.

Loki Pedley (6)
Beanfield Primary School, Corby

The Giraffe

My creature is a giraffe
She has lots of spots
She lives in the zoo
She eats leaves off the tree
She thinks that she is a dog.

Evie-Rose Sharpe (6)
Beanfield Primary School, Corby

My Pokémon

My Pokémon is cute
He is called Pikachu
He is good
He plays with everyone
He likes to play with his friends.

Lucas G (5)
Beanfield Primary School, Corby

Horse

H is for horse
O is for orange
R is for rocky
S is for soars
E is for exciting.

Shaylene Burbidge (6)
Beanfield Primary School, Corby

The Butterfly

My butterfly lives in the jungle
He can dance
He likes to eat chocolate ice cream
He likes to fly
He looks cute.

Lilly Higgins (6)
Beanfield Primary School, Corby

Cute Panda

My creature is a panda
She has lots of spots
She lives in the jungle
She eats bamboo
She sleeps in the jungle.

Jessica Brown (6)
Beanfield Primary School, Corby

Butterfly

My creature is a butterfly
She lives in trees
And sleeps in twigs and leaves
She is small
She likes to eat.

Olivia Graham (5)
Beanfield Primary School, Corby

The Fox

My creature is a fox
He has lots of hair
He is fast asleep
He lives in the forest
He likes to eat chicken.

Chiril Bulubica (5)
Beanfield Primary School, Corby

Unicorn

My creature is a unicorn
He has lots of fluffy hair
He lives in the wild, under rocks
And likes to eat pizza.

Grace Mitchell (6)
Beanfield Primary School, Corby

Horse

My creature is a horse
She has lots of stripes
She lives on a farm
And it eats grass
She likes to run.

Alayah Montgomery (5)
Beanfield Primary School, Corby

The Butterfly

My creature is a butterfly
He has lots of colours
He lives in the pretty jungle
He likes to eat chocolate.

Layla Ruffel (5)
Beanfield Primary School, Corby

Bear

My creature is a bear
He has lots of fluffy hair
He likes to eat honey
My creature likes to climb trees.

Brooklyn Cooper-Mason (5)
Beanfield Primary School, Corby

The Cow

My creature is a cow
She has lots of spots
She lives on a farm
And she likes to eat grass.

Livvi Pedley (6)
Beanfield Primary School, Corby

The Rattlesnake

My insect is a snake
He has sharp teeth
He lives in the zoo
And he eats cheeseburgers.

John Montgomery (6)
Beanfield Primary School, Corby

My Cat

My animal is a cat
He has to go to dance
He eats doughnuts
And likes to sing.

Martins Vecais (5)
Beanfield Primary School, Corby

The Tiger

The animals are scared of the tiger
But he eats people
And he plays with toys.

Bianca Caraus (6) & Catrina
Beanfield Primary School, Corby

Penguin

My creature is a penguin
He has
He lives
And
He likes to eat fish.

Lacie-Mae Moore (6)
Beanfield Primary School, Corby

Giraffe

My creature is a giraffe
He has a lot of spots
He lives under the rocks.

Dominik Swidrski (6)
Beanfield Primary School, Corby

Dog

Dogs are soft
Its colour is black
My dog is smart
My dog is soft.

Alise Silina (6)
Beanfield Primary School, Corby

Fast Dog

D ogs can run fast
O dd dog
G ood boy.

Charlie London (7)
Beanfield Primary School, Corby

Dog

a **D** orable
O wner it has
G orgeous.

Samantha Eliza Kreslina (7)
Beanfield Primary School, Corby

My Jaguar Poem

I'm a fierce jaguar
I like to run a lot
I move around
So I can get very hot
Every time an animal passes
I pounce on it for tea
I don't think anyone could even notice me
I am very fast
As fast as a flying flea
Nobody could even be as fast as me
When there is meat around
I run and pounce on the ground
Watch out for my claws
Just wait till you hear the snapping of my jaws
I live in the rainforest
What a wonderful place to be
I wonder what will happen next, let's go see.

Sophie Nicholson (7)
Bishopsgate School, Englefield Green

Jaguar Poem

I am a fierce jaguar
Under the leaves, I prowl
I go into the water to get cool
And growl so loud that the animals hide
A lonely gazelle I spied
I let out one of my biggest growls
The gazelle let out a howl
That's my lunch, did you hear me crunch?
Toucans and macaw glide through the air
I always find the sloths and gobble their
hair
I leap and stalk my prey
My spots are black and grey
So I am camouflaged in dead leaves
I hunt for my prey in the trees for tea
In my cave, I sunbathe!

Yuvi Uppal (6)
Bishopsgate School, Englefield Green

The Jaguar

In the rainforest, you might see
Bright green, leafy, tall trees
Squawks from toucans
Leaves bigger than your head
Wet, watery waterfalls
Great, green, grassy bushes
A jaguar prowling around
It doesn't make a sound
Hunting a bird, about to pounce
It has sharp teeth and claws
It had a huge body
Yellow with black rosettes
Eyes as green as grass
The jaguar, ready to pounce
The jaguar pounced and ate its prey
He won't need to eat for a day.

Isobel Massie (7)
Bishopsgate School, Englefield Green

A Jaguar In The Rainforest

In the rainforest, you might see
Some brown, mossy sloths
Munching on some leaves
Or some wet, leafy trees
As brown as chocolate chips
Some pretty pink flowers
Waving about in the wind
Then silently creeps the jaguar
All the animals hide
With yellow, spotty fur
It's as quiet as a mouse
Viciously creeping to hunt for its tea
A bright, colourful toucan flying across the
sky
Making loud noises as he passes by.

Marla Johal (7)
Bishopsgate School, Englefield Green

The Rainforest

In the rainforest, you might see
Some fluffy, buzzing bees
Leaves flowing in the wind
While the birds squawk
The smooth and colourful
Boa constrictor
Scales as pointy as a knife
Is hunting for its prey
It sees a small mouse
It waits until it pounces
It grabs and squeezes
And bites until death
It happily eats its dinner
While staring into the rainforest
He hears something
A puma attacks...

Charl Marais (7)
Bishopsgate School, Englefield Green

The Rainforest

The rainforest is thick, spooky and dark
Trees as tall as mountains
Boa constrictors slithering on the floor
Quick, look! A black spotty coat
An orange, fluffy coat
Eyes twinkle in the sun
What is it? It's a jaguar!
Waiting patiently, ready to pounce
A horrifying jaguar slowly creeping towards you
A jaguar pouncing up into the air, silently catching a toucan.

Grayson Webb (7)
Bishopsgate School, Englefield Green

The Jaguar Poem

I'm a jaguar with lots of spots
I hunt, looking for my prey
It's fun to hunt when you live next to the
kapok tree
I like to eat sloths who live in the trees
And loads of other animals like monkeys
and fleas
In the day, I'm on the ground
At night, I sleep without a sound
I am very camouflaged and hairy
To other animals, I'm so scary.

Joshua Dean (7)
Bishopsgate School, Englefield Green

My Sloth Poem

I am a sloth
I am very slow
Where would I live if I have no glow?
I climb up high, trying to reach the sky
I can't come down because I'm too shy
I am so lazy
People think I'm crazy
I swing from the trees and sway
I just hang around all day
In the Amazon rainforest
You will find me
Have a look at the tallest tree!

Simran Kapila (6)
Bishopsgate School, Englefield Green

Jaguar

I am a fierce, brave jaguar
I hunt for my prey
Lazing around all day
And then killing my prey
In front of my cave
I like to bathe
When I go hunting at the night
I kill my prey in one bite
My furry coat is so sleek
I am very strong, not weak
The bigger animals won't come near me
Watch out! I'm ready for my tea!

Henry Stannard (7)
Bishopsgate School, Englefield Green

The Jaguar

In the rainforest, you might see
Puffy and fluffy, scary animals
The trees are tall and damp
Jaguars as quick as a leopard
With spots as dark as night
Eyes as blue as a river
And teeth as sharp as swords
Creeping silently to the floor
Trying to start a war
Trees rustling in the wind
Rocks rolling on the ground everywhere.

Ruby Carver (7)
Bishopsgate School, Englefield Green

My Macaw Poem

I'm a fast, colourful macaw
I have a very small jaw
I have a backwards claw
I'm very good at swooping from tree to tree
Looking for things to eat just for me
I see lots of leaves
In the big, gigantic trees in the emergent layer
Up, up high in the sky which makes me lucky
As I'm far away from danger.

Joshua Jacobi (7)
Bishopsgate School, Englefield Green

The Toucan

In the rainforest, you might see
Trees as tall as mountains
Buzzy bees
Berries as blue as the sky
Big, flying birds and scary animals too
You will find toucans
As noisy as an elephant trumpeting
Flying from tree to tree
With monkeys swinging on the vines
Colourful toucans make the Amazon
beautiful.

Lian Louw (7)
Bishopsgate School, Englefield Green

The Toucan

In the rainforest, you might see
Lots and lots of tall green trees
A cute green toucan sitting upon her nest
Keeping her eggs warm and having a rest
She has a long orange beak
And is loud with a squeak
She is happy in the branches among the
flowers
In the deep, dark rainforest, wet with
showers.

Diya Khosla (6)
Bishopsgate School, Englefield Green

Jungle Dreams

A snake called Jake
Lived by a sparkling lake
He baked delicious cakes
A monkey swung by, up high
Trying to fly
A fabulous macaw
Was trying to roar
But she had a tiny jaw
A slimy frog
Was trying to jog
Along a slippery log
A posh sloth
Was trying to make a tablecloth!

Claudia Priestley (7)
Bishopsgate School, Englefield Green

The Rainforest

In the rainforest, you might see
lots of animals and very tall trees

In the rainforest, you might see
gorillas, colourful birds and even
chimpanzees

In the rainforest, you might also see
big, huge bumblebees

So why don't you come to the rainforest
and explore with me.

Kye Saavan Shipp (7)
Bishopsgate School, Englefield Green

My Sloth Poem

When I hide up in the trees
The jaguars always find me
And they gobble me up
In their big, bad jaws
While I'm in the wars
Life in the rainforest is tough
And all the jaguars are so rough
I can't take them down
And I always have a frown
That's the life of a sloth.

Verity Taylor (7)
Bishopsgate School, Englefield Green

The Rainforest

In the rainforest, you might see
Lovely, beautiful birds
Singing in the tall, tall trees.
The boa constrictor gets ready to pounce.
The jaguar is sleeping under big, big leaves.
The boa constrictor is lurking across
The slippery forest floor.
The boa constrictor slides and leaves...

Misha Ffrench (7)
Bishopsgate School, Englefield Green

Scary Jaguar

I am a scary jaguar
I am enormous and fierce
In the sunshine, I lay
Living in the rainforest
I look kind but I can hurt you
Hunting for deer, monkeys and birds
I rest when I am full
My coat is pretty
Because of my spots
I'm brave and fat
And lazy like a cat!

Rose Gurney (7)
Bishopsgate School, Englefield Green

My Jaguar Poem

The jaguar creeps,
The jaguar crawls,
The jaguar is fed up
With what animals call.
He hunts for his prey
Day after day.
Climbing high up to the sky
He lets out a sigh.
What was that shout?
I have a big doubt.
Well, back to my home
All alone!

William McCauley-Tinniswood (7)
Bishopsgate School, Englefield Green

The Sloth

In the rainforest, you might see
Tall, tall trees
Wet, damp leaves
Muddy, wet ground
The sloth munches a juicy green leaf
Slowly climbing down
He hangs upside down
Sliding from tree to tree
The jaguar lurks in the forest
Slowly looking for its prey.

Eoin O'Brien (7)
Bishopsgate School, Englefield Green

The Rainforest

In the rainforest, you might see
Dark, wet, leafy bushes and tall, tall trees
Animals as small as a mouse or as a house
Lazy sloth lays as still as a leaf on the ground
It climbs down the tree as slowly as a snail
Hanging upside down, eating big, green, juicy leaves.

Evie Wheaton (7)
Bishopsgate School, Englefield Green

The Butterfly

The beautiful light butterfly
Takes her flight with delight
She flaps her beautiful wings
And dances and dazzles all sorts of things
Toucans, jaguars and bees
The snakes climbing up the trees
Life in the Amazon rainforest is good
Come and visit, I would!

Isabelle Baldwin (7)
Bishopsgate School, Englefield Green

The Rainforest

In the rainforest, you might see
tall trees and damp and squelchy mud.

Leaves as green as peas.
You can hear water splashing.

Up in the canopy, rests a lazy sloth,
munching on a green leaf.
He slowly goes down, eating more from the
ground.

Shivani Mistry (7)
Bishopsgate School, Englefield Green

The Boa Constrictor

In the rainforest, you might see
Wet, leafy, tall trees
And buzzy, buzzy bees
The boa constrictor lies still
Waiting for his prey
It slithers along the forest floor
It is sneaky and slinky for sure
Jaguar, black and orange
Standing silently.

Dominic Butler (7)
Bishopsgate School, Englefield Green

My Sloth Poem

I'm a lazy sloth
My fur is brown
I like to catch moths
But they make me frown
I swing in the trees way up high
I watch as the macaw and toucan fly on by
I move very slowly and I live in a tree
If you look very carefully
You will see me!

Nimrit Sindher (6)
Bishopsgate School, Englefield Green

120

Macaws

I am a macaw with a very strong jaw
And a backwards claw
I live in the rainforest
And my best friend is Boris
I'm colourful from head to toe
Glide and swoop, watch my show
Eat berries and seeds
Find me in the tallest trees.

Aryun Rabheru (6)
Bishopsgate School, Englefield Green

Macaws

I am a blue macaw
I have a small jaw
I also have a backwards claw
I use my beak to crack nuts and seed
Then I fly back into the green trees
The feathers on my back
Are bright and colourful
That makes me very happy and joyful!

Ronnie Bannister (7)
Bishopsgate School, Englefield Green

The Rainforest

In the forest, you might see
Dark, wet leaves
Tall, tall trees
You might see fluffy, big animals
And bright colourful toucans
Flying from tree to tree
Squawking loudly over waterfalls
Their beaks as bright as a light.

Erin Long (7)
Bishopsgate School, Englefield Green

A Bad Jaguar Poem

I am a bad jaguar
I love to hunt
Look out!
You might be my lunch
If you see my paws
You will hear me roar
Watch out, zebras and deer
I am prowling near you
Can't get away
Or I will be back another day.

Sofia Rai (7)
Bishopsgate School, Englefield Green

124

My Toucan Poem

I am a toucan
I like to sleep in the morning
An early start gets me yawning
It is such a delight to see
All the wonderful sights
I can see nice trees and leaves
Did you know I can fly so high
My wings touch the sky?

Arjan Auluck (7)
Bishopsgate School, Englefield Green

Squirrel Monkey

Squirrel monkey, squirrel monkey
Fly in the tree

Squirrel monkey, squirrel monkey
Buzzing like a bee

They jump, they swing, run and laugh
They get very dirty and now they need a
bath!

Andrey Olney (9)
Bishopsgate School, Englefield Green

The Sloth

As slow as a snail, the sloth moves along
Clinging to the trees where it belongs
The sloth swings down to the forest floor
Munching on crunchy leaves
He loves more and more.

Henry Stere (7)
Bishopsgate School, Englefield Green

The Jaguar

Long, tall trees in the rainforest
Jaguars are strong and long
Munching on animals
With sharp claws
She is just like a bunny
Hunting and panting in the tall grass.

Maisie Lockyer (6)
Bishopsgate School, Englefield Green

The Rainforest

In the rainforest, you might see
Big trees and noisy rain
Huge leafy bushes
Trees as big as me
Spotty jaguars
Hairy, scary jaguars
Fast and fierce jaguars.

Karamvir Singh Athwal (7)
Bishopsgate School, Englefield Green

My Animal Riddle

As energetic as a horse
It eats carrots and hay
It can run really fast
As cute as a hamster
People ride on its back
It has four legs
As furry as a cat.

What is it?

Hephzibah A (6)
Marton Primary Academy, Marton

My Riddle

It has a collar
It is cute and cuddly
There are people who live with it
As cute as a baby

What is it?
It is Cookie, my special dog.

Mylee J (6)
Marton Primary Academy, Marton

My Cute Animal

It has a collar
It comes in different colours
As cute as a cat
It goes *ruff! Ruff! Ruff!*

What is it?
It is a dog.

Annabelle B (6)

Marton Primary Academy, Marton

My Riddle

My animal lives in a hole
My animal eats rats
It is as long as a rope
It has a wiggly body

What is it?
It is a snake.

Olivia S (6)
Marton Primary Academy, Marton

What Am I?

It has green skin
It is long and stretchy
It is slippery and poisonous
As long as a rope

What is it?
It is a snake.

Presley Marshall (6)
Marton Primary Academy, Marton

What Am I?

It has floppy ears
It is fluffy and cute
Its nose twitches
As soft as a cotton wool ball

What is it?
It is a bunny.

Ellie C (6)

Marton Primary Academy, Marton

My Animal Riddle

As cute as a hamster
As fast as a poodle
Lives in a black cage
Runs, jumps and cries

What is it?
It is a dog.

Fatoumatta C (6)
Marton Primary Academy, Marton

What Am I?

It has sharp claws
It is brown and white
Its fur is fluffy
As fast as a motorbike

What is it?
It is a cat.

Caleb H (6)

Marton Primary Academy, Marton

What Am I?

It has four feet
It is soft and fluffy
Its fur is white
As white as a polar bear

What is it?
It is a dog.

Henry A (5)
Marton Primary Academy, Marton

My Riddle

It is rare because it is gold
Its horn is magical
The horn makes cupcakes

What is it?
It is a magical unicorn.

Elizabeth H (5)
Marton Primary Academy, Marton

My Pet

It has a furry tail
It is as cute as a cat
It is beautiful
As furry as a wolf

What is it?
It is a dog.

Hugo Hoogerwerf (6)
Marton Primary Academy, Marton

What Am I?

It has small fluffy legs
It is fluffy
Its tail is long
As small as a mouse

What is it?
It is a kitten.

Matilda H (6)
Marton Primary Academy, Marton

My Riddle

It is magnificent
It is amazing
It is beautiful
It flies like a bird

What is it?
It is a unicorn.

Amelia M (6)
Marton Primary Academy, Marton

My Animal

It can climb walls
It is fast
It is scary
It is as fast as a cheetah

What is it?
It is a spider.

Haniel A (6)

Marton Primary Academy, Marton

What Am I?

It has a fluffy tail
It is soft
Its food is carrots
As cute as a baby

What is it?
It is a bunny.

Lexie Fox (5)

Marton Primary Academy, Marton

What Am I?

It has a beak
It is soft
Its wings are big
As fluffy as a pillow

What is it?
It is a snowy owl.

Lenny Gelder (6)
Marton Primary Academy, Marton

My Animal

It has wings and a horn
It is rare and magical
As beautiful as a flower

What is it?
It is a unicorn.

Maizie B (5)
Marton Primary Academy, Marton

My Riddle

It has a mane
It is magnificent
Its claws are sharp
As fast as a car

What is it?
It is a lion.

Logan M (6)

Marton Primary Academy, Marton

What Am I?

It has no legs
It is very fast
Its skin is slimy
As long as an eel

What is it?
It is a snake.

Jake M (6)
Marton Primary Academy, Marton

What Am I?

It has claws
It is stripy
Its body is huge
As loud as a roar

What is it?
It is a tiger.

Dylan-James Brannan (6)
Marton Primary Academy, Marton

What Am I?

It has grey fur
It is funny
Its fur is soft
As soft as a cat

What is it?
It is a dog.

Imogen Phillips (5)
Marton Primary Academy, Marton

My Animal Riddle

It is scaly as a mermaid
It has gold skin
It swims in a tank

What is it?
It is a goldfish.

Alysia Mccoy (6)
Marton Primary Academy, Marton

My Animal Riddle

It has small black legs
It is fast
Its home is in the soil
What is it?
It is an ant.

Kyle M (6)
Marton Primary Academy, Marton

My Riddle

I am dangerous, scary and a bit fat
I live in a hot place
I have yellow and orange skin
I eat gazelle meat and chickens
Have you guessed what I am yet?
I have a mane and a tail
I use my claws to eat my food
My yellow skin helps me to hide
I hate tigers, people and pigeons
I love zebras because they give me meat
If you ever met me
You'd think I am scary, mean and bad
Do you know I can eat people?
What am I?
I am a lion.

Evan Moran (7)
Shakespeare Primary School, Fleetwood

What Am I?

I am cute and sticky
I love to climb on stuff
I live in trees and soft, lovely leaves
I eat juicy, squidgy leaves
Have you guessed what I am?
I love to climb on people's hands
I use their clothes just to climb on walls
I hate meat and sugar
I love to climb on stuff
If you see me, you might be scared
Did you know my name backwards is insect stick?
It's good to be me
Because I can climb like a monkey
Oh, I forgot to mention
I am brown and green
I wish I could swim

Here's a funky fact
I have four legs and antenna
What am I?
I am a stick insect.

Cody Kennedy (7)
Shakespeare Primary School, Fleetwood

What Am I?

I am cute and spotty
I live in the wild
I eat leaves and greenflies
Have you guessed what I am yet?
I have a lot of friends that look like me
I use logs to get to high places
I hate water
I love leaves and greenflies
If you met me, you'd think I'm really cute
Did you know a group of me is called a
bloom?
It's good to be me because I can
camouflage
Oh, I forgot to mention, I'm red
I enjoy crawling about and eating
I wish I could swim for a day
I am red and spotty

What am I?
I am a ladybird.

Amity Crellin (7)
Shakespeare Primary School, Fleetwood

What Am I?

I am mean and yellow
I live in Africa with elephants
It's good to be me
Because I can eat other animals
I am a carnivore
Have you guessed what I am yet?
I eat meat and I hate water
If you ever see me, you would run
Oh, I forgot to mention
I hunt down other animals
You wouldn't want to stroke me
I would eat you
A group of me is a pack
I wish I could eat human food for a day
It is good to be me
Because I can sneak up on other animals
I have hair around my head

What am I?
I am a lion.

Zac Newton (7)
Shakespeare Primary School, Fleetwood

My Riddle

I am as black as the night but kind.
I live in a dark, dark cave in the woods.
I eat flesh to feed my family and cub.
Have you guessed what I am yet?
I have a nice, helpful family and cub.
I use my fur coat to keep me warm,
I hate intruders in my home.
I love my family more than food.
If you ever met me you would think
I am scary but I am really nice.
Did you know that I can run one mile per
hour?
What am I?
I am a wolf.

Summer Hill (7)
Shakespeare Primary School, Fleetwood

What Am I?

I live in the desert or in a forest
I hate water, every time I have a bath
I don't like it
I have a shell to hide
If a predator is around I can hide
I am green and I have four legs
I hibernate
I love pak choi because it is tasty
Here's a funky fact
I am slow, cute and small
Do you need another clue?
What am I?
I am a tortoise.

Jaxon Smith (7)
Shakespeare Primary School, Fleetwood

My Riddle

I am cute
You would love to have me as a pet
I eat hay
I live on a farm
Have you guessed what I am yet?
I have a neck almost as long as a giraffe's
I used a saddle and bridle and saddle pad
I hate having a bath
I love carrots
If you ever met me you would love me and
want me
Did you know I am very fast?
What am I?
I am a horse.

Teddy Bamber (7)
Shakespeare Primary School, Fleetwood

What Am I?

I am 100 years old
I wiggle my fin
I am scary
I am fierce
Have you guessed what I am yet?
I live in the sea
I swim in the sea
I am blue
I forgot to mention
That I eat fish
I eat humans too
Have you guessed what I am yet?
Do you need another clue?
I am in a famous film called Jaws
What am I?
I am a shark.

Sophie Myers (7)
Shakespeare Primary School, Fleetwood

What Am I?

Did you know that I am massive?
I wish I could survive every day, but I can't
Did you know I am fat?
I love to eat meat for a treat only
I have sharp teeth
If you met me, you would run away
Did you know a bunch of me is called a
herd?
It's good to be me because I can chomp
Have you guessed what I am yet?
I am a dinosaur.

Carson Stone (6)
Shakespeare Primary School, Fleetwood

My Riddle

I am a fish and I love the water
I live in the tank and I swim in the tank
I eat fish food
Have you guessed what I am yet?
I have a fish tank
I have nothing to use
I hate sharks
I love swimming in the water
If you met me you'd think I look cute
Did you know that I think I love tanks?
What am I?
I am a goldfish.

Raya Yordanova (6)
Shakespeare Primary School, Fleetwood

What Am I?

I am big and cute
I eat sometimes in the water
But it is hard to catch
I live somewhere snowy
If you met me
You would run away from me
Where I live is very cold
Have you guessed what I am yet?
It's good to be me
Because I don't have to do chores
I have a black nose
What am I?
I am a polar bear.

Olivia Coe (7)
Shakespeare Primary School, Fleetwood

What Am I?

I am spotty and yellow
I live in the woods
I eat meat
Have you guessed what I am yet?
I have sharp claws to kill animals
I hate the animals that I eat
I love how fast I can run
If you ever met me you'd think that I am dangerous
Did you know that I am faster than a racing car?
What am I?
I am a leopard.

Toby Smith
Shakespeare Primary School, Fleetwood

What Am I?

I am cheeky and I drink water
I have lots of energy
I can be black and brown
I run fast
For a treat, I have a banana
I love jumping up
Do you need another clue?
If you dare me to never climb trees
I will probably break that
I am little
I am very cute
What am I?
I am a monkey.

Corey (7)
Shakespeare Primary School, Fleetwood

What Am I?

I am harmless, cute and long
I have spikes on the side of me
I live in the desert or a tank
With a heat lamp
I eat meat, fruit and vegetables
I hate baths
I will just climb out
I wish I had wings so I could fly and swim
I am cold-blooded
I am a reptile
What am I?
I am a lizard.

Harley Holt (7)
Shakespeare Primary School, Fleetwood

My Riddle

I live in a long, yellow and tiring desert
I eat fish
Have you guessed what I am yet?
I have a bright orange beak
I use my legs to run very fast
I hate seeds
I love to run
If you met me you'd think I am crazy
Did you know I can run very fast?
What am I?
I am an ostrich.

Jenson Gray (6)
Shakespeare Primary School, Fleetwood

My Riddle

I am weird, funny, crazy and tall
I live under the bed
I eat schools, bread and Tango
I have a shark fin and a pig body
I use an iPhone
I love burgers
If you met me you'd think
Why did I come here?
Did you know I am very tall?
What am I?
I am a shimmy.

Millie Potter (7)
Shakespeare Primary School, Fleetwood

My Riddle

I am tall, stripy and grey
I live in a creepy dark cave
I eat bacon and dry bread
Have you guessed what I am yet?
I have white wings
I hate fish
I love my beautiful family
If you met me you'd think I'm terrifying
Did you know I can fly to the clouds?
What am I?

Sophie Davies (7)
Shakespeare Primary School, Fleetwood

What Am I?

I use my paws to walk
I can walk fast
Did you know
If you see me, you better run
I wish I could be in the circus
I am super furry
I am harmful so don't annoy me
My name backwards is noil
I am in a film, The Lion King
What am I?
I am a lion.

Jackson Armstrong (7)
Shakespeare Primary School, Fleetwood

What Am I?

I love catching fish
Sometimes I sleep
I love to do tricks and I love to swim
I only live underwater
I wish to go on land for one day
I have a fin
It's good to be me
Because I can swim fast
I am very clever
What am I?
I am a dolphin.

Eliza Magowan (6)
Shakespeare Primary School, Fleetwood

Hamster

My hamster has a wheel
And goes round and round
She likes eating hamster food
She is always in a good mood
She likes to sleep in the day
Then at night, she likes to play.

Amelia Whiteshide-Shaw (6)
Shakespeare Primary School, Fleetwood

What Is It?

It has a mane
It is dark orange
It can roar
It eats meat
It can jump far
It can run fast

What is it?
It is a lion.

Elijah Armstrong (6)
Shakespeare Primary School, Fleetwood

Cat

My cat has a long tail
He likes eating cat food with a snail
My cat likes eating seagulls on a throne
He does not like eating on his own.

Emilia Maricic (5)
Shakespeare Primary School, Fleetwood

What Is It?

It has a long neck
It has small ears
It is yellow and brown
It has a long tongue

What is it?
It is a giraffe.

Holly Emslie (6)
Shakespeare Primary School, Fleetwood

What Is It?

It is orange
It hops
It has a pouch with a baby
It has a strong kick

What is it?
It is a kangaroo.

Reuben Yardley (6)
Shakespeare Primary School, Fleetwood

Fish

My fish is as colourful as a unicorn
She likes to swim round and round
She is the best fish I have ever had.

Beth Williamson (6)

Shakespeare Primary School, Fleetwood

What Is It?

It has big ears
It is grey
It is huge
It has a trunk

What is it?
It is an elephant.

Rose Stirzaker (6)
Shakespeare Primary School, Fleetwood

Polar Bear

He's white and bright
Massive is his might
And makes us shiver with fright
He can swim and hunt prey
On a whim
He lives in the North Pole
And sleeping through the winter
Is his goal
He sleeps on ice
And he is not very nice
Seals are his happy meal
Soft and furry is how he will feel
He lives in the ice
White is his disguise
Ice is where he hunts
But what will he do
When it all melts?

Janvika Jagadeesh (5)
Springfield Primary School, Sunbury-On-Thames

The Hungry Lion

Lion, lion, what do you hear?
I hear my tummy rumble,
The animals run in fear.
Lion, lion, what do you think?
I'm going to hunt,
And then get a drink.
Lion, lion, what do you see?
I see a black and white zebra,
All for me.
Lion, lion, what do you feel?
Great! The wind in my face,
I forgot to hunt.
The zebra got away,
That was my meal!

Max Honey (7)
Springfield Primary School, Sunbury-On-Thames

Tiger's Friend

Tiger had a friend
He was scared of Tiger
Tiger looked after him
Can you guess what animal it is?
It is a monkey.

Monkey is naughty
Monkey is fun
Monkey had a big bum
Monkey sits in the tree
While he watches and sees
Then he sees Tiger
He gives him a hug
Squeeze! Squeeze!
I love you, Snug!

Prem Chouhan (7)
Springfield Primary School, Sunbury-On-Thames

All About Koalas

Koalas are cute
Koalas are snuggly
They are very fluffy
They eat eucalyptus
They are very, very soft
They are beautiful
They live in trees
They are found in Australia
They like to climb trees
Babies are called Joeys
They live in their mother's pouch
They are pretty
They are fuzzy.

Leah Midwinter (7)
Springfield Primary School, Sunbury-On-Thames

Dear Ladybug

Dear ladybug
I don't always see you in my garden
But when I do, I say hello to you
Dear ladybug
I would love to give you a hug
When I get too close
You spread your spotty wings
And flutter away on the summer wind
Dear ladybug
Thank you for making my day brighter.

Dominic Germishuys (7)
Springfield Primary School, Sunbury-On-Thames

Facts About Tigers

T here is a country where most of them live, it is Asia.

I know that tigers are carnivorous and they have sharp teeth.

G rowls of a tiger are even louder than a bear's growls.

E very time I see a tiger, I get excited.

R oar! is the sound that tigers make.

Leila Aghel (7)

Springfield Primary School, Sunbury-On-Thames

Flamingo

Flamingoes are pink
Flamingoes are tall
You find flamingoes
In the zoo, zoo, zoo

Flamingoes have wings
Flamingoes eat fish
You can find them mostly
By the water, water, water.

Sophie O'Donnell (5)
Springfield Primary School, Sunbury-On-Thames

Oh Butterfly

Oh butterfly, oh butterfly,
you make the world so colourful!
Oh butterfly, oh butterfly,
you fly so high!
Oh butterfly, oh butterfly,
you are so beautiful!
Oh butterfly, oh butterfly.

Zainab Naqvi (6)
Springfield Primary School, Sunbury-On-Thames

The Hairy, Scary Spider

The hairy, scary spider
Works hard on his web
The hairy, scary spider
Is waiting to be fed.

James Lee (6)
Springfield Primary School, Sunbury-On-Thames

Giraffe

G iraffes have

I ncredible long necks

R un 35 miles an hour

A re very tall

F emales are called cows

F ive to 30 minutes' sleep a day

E at leaves and shoots.

Annie McConville (7)

St Mary's Primary School Dunsford, Ardglass

What Is It?

As cute as a unicorn
As elegant as the first lady
As clever as a scientist
As fast as a shark
As smooth as an octopus
It swims like a turtle
Playful when it sees humans
It's a dolphin.

Nicole Karbauske (7)
St Mary's Primary School Dunsford, Ardglass

What Am I?

As beautiful as a summer's day
As elegant as the queen
As clever as a genius
As graceful as a butterfly
As wet as the ocean
As playful as a pup

What am I?
A dolphin!

Isla O'Connor (7)
St Mary's Primary School Dunsford, Ardglass

What Am I?

As fast as a cheetah
As clever as my teacher
As beautiful as a baby
As white as the snow
As deadly as a crocodile
As cute as a diamond

What am I?
A white tiger.

James McGreevy (7)
St Mary's Primary School Dunsford, Ardglass

Horse

H appy days are coming
O ver fences and fields
R oaming freely with others
S unshine and laughter
E venings with clear blue skies for riding.

Izzy Burns (7)
St Mary's Primary School Dunsford, Ardglass

What Am I?

As elegant as my mummy
As grey as a rock
As wrinkled as a crushed-up shirt
As smart as my sister
As loud as can be

What am I?
An elephant!

Stella Zych (7)
St Mary's Primary School Dunsford, Ardglass

What Is It?

As black as the coal in my fire
As warm as the sun
As fast as my brother
As cuddly as my teddy
It's my dog, Shadow!

Madden McEvoy (7)
St Mary's Primary School Dunsford, Ardglass

What Is It?

As cute as a puppy
As white as the snow
As slow as a turtle
Looks like my dad dressed up
It's a penguin.

Callum Moreland (7)
St Mary's Primary School Dunsford, Ardglass

What Is It?

As fast as a butterfly
As beautiful as a summer's day
As colourful as a rainbow
It's a lion!

Amelia Feenan (7)

St Mary's Primary School Dunsford, Ardglass

What Is It?

As big as my Jeep
As fluffy as the clouds
As cheeky as my cat
It's a bear!

Eabha O'Connor (6)
St Mary's Primary School Dunsford, Ardglass

My Penguin Poem

My penguin is black and white
My penguin has an orange beak
My penguin feels cold and slippery
My penguin smells like fish
My penguin tastes salty
My penguin goes *beep! Beep!*

Charlie Wood (5)
Westwood Primary School, Leeds

My Cow Poem

My cow looks red and green with black spots
My cow smells like milk
My cow feels like ice and cheese
My cow sounds like a stomping dinosaur
My cow tastes like bananas.

Wyatt Hitchcox (6)

Westwood Primary School, Leeds

Lizard

As scaly as a snake
As slippery as a lizard's tail
As cheeky as a smelly monkey
As sneaky as an ant
As naughty as a rat and a mouse
It is a lizard.

Bobby Keeligan (6)

Westwood Primary School, Leeds

Butterfly Poem

My butterfly is pretty
My butterfly is happy
She likes to fly
She smells like ice cream
She feels like soft silk
She tastes like cheese pizza.

Blake Scaife (6)
Westwood Primary School, Leeds

My Dog Poem

My dog looks cute
She smells like flowers and ice cream
She feels soft and cuddly
She sounds like a noisy class
She tastes like ice cream.

Rose Cummings (6)
Westwood Primary School, Leeds

Icing Cat

My icing cat is rainbow and is happy
She smells like chips
She is fluffy like a cloud
She tastes like ice cream and sprinkles.

Lucii Batley-Hewitt (5)
Westwood Primary School, Leeds

What Am I?

As strong as an elephant
As interesting as the Queen
As gigantic as Asia
As hungry as my tummy
I am a giraffe.

Harley Cross (6)
Westwood Primary School, Leeds

The Butterfly

As unique as a unicorn
As pretty as a flower
As delightful as a vase
As beautiful as a rose
I am a butterfly.

Tilly Gudgeon (7)
Westwood Primary School, Leeds

My Dog Poem

He is big and fluffy
He smells of bones
He feels soft and cold
He tastes like dog food
He sounds like a bark.

Aleksei Beloussov (6)
Westwood Primary School, Leeds

What Am I?

As lazy as a very old elephant
As cheeky as a baby monkey
As soft as a polar bear's fluffy fur
I am a sloth.

Tyreece Whitley (6)
Westwood Primary School, Leeds

What Am I?

As delicate as a golden statue
As elegant as a princess
As beautiful as a dandelion flower
I am a butterfly.

Mutiat Kumoye (6)
Westwood Primary School, Leeds

Mia Cat Poem

My Mia cat is long and blue
She likes to jump
She smells like ice cream
She feels like a fluffy pillow.

Mia Hart-Kumar (6)
Westwood Primary School, Leeds

My Mouse Poem

Smells like chicken
Feels soft and warm
Tastes like strawberries
Looks fun
Sounds scratchy.

BooBoo Hallas (6)
Westwood Primary School, Leeds

What Is It?

As rough as a sheet of metal
It is as poisonous as a rattlesnake
As mysterious as a mythical dragon.

George Richardson (6)
Westwood Primary School, Leeds

What Am I?

Claws are sharp
It is big
It is strong
It is scary
It eats meat
It can climb trees.

Jacob Egan (7)
Westwood Primary School, Leeds

What Am I?

As scary as a snappy crocodile
Claws as sharp as a knife
As sneaky as a monkey
I am a tiger.

Amelia Holmes (6)
Westwood Primary School, Leeds

What Am I?

I am as snuggly as snow
As cuddly as a teddy bear
As lazy as a cute koala
I am a sloth.

Joey Baker (6)
Westwood Primary School, Leeds

What Am I?

As soft as a hairy foot
As small as a mouse
As cheeky as my best friend
I am a monkey.

George Kenyon (6)
Westwood Primary School, Leeds

What Am I?

As strong as Godzilla
As scary as a crocodile
As big as a dragon
I am a tiger.

Deacon Massey (6)
Westwood Primary School, Leeds

What Am I?

As hairy as a bear
As strong as King Kong
As large as a house
I am a lion.

TreydenThomas Appleyard (7)
Westwood Primary School, Leeds

What Am I?

As big as Godzilla
As hungry as a lion
As strong as a boxer
I am a lion.

Leo Brummitt (6)
Westwood Primary School, Leeds

My Cat Poem

It smells like peppermint
It looks like a black pen
It tastes like chocolate.

Lorna Walton (5)
Westwood Primary School, Leeds

My Giraffe Poem

It smells like sweet candy
It looks like a rainbow
It tastes like Skittles.

Ebonie Wager (6)
Westwood Primary School, Leeds

What Am I?

As vicious as a killer whale
As strong as a tractor
As big as an elephant.

Sam Avison (7)
Westwood Primary School, Leeds

My Penguin

Penguins smell like fish and chips
It is fluffy
It is black and white.

Oliver Coghill (6)
Westwood Primary School, Leeds

YOUNG WRITERS
INFORMATION

We hope you have enjoyed reading this book – and that you will continue to in the coming years.

If you're the parent or family member of an enthusiastic poet or story writer, do visit our website **www.youngwriters.co.uk/subscribe** and sign up to receive news, competitions, writing challenges and tips, activities and much, much more! There's lots to keep budding writers motivated!

If you would like to order further copies of this book, or any of our other titles, then please give us a call or order via your online account.

Young Writers
Remus House
Coltsfoot Drive
Peterborough
PE2 9BF
(01733) 890066
info@youngwriters.co.uk

Join in the conversation!
Tips, news, giveaways and much more!

 YoungWritersUK  YoungWritersCW 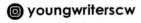 youngwriterscw